NINJA ENEMIES

WRITTEN BY
BETH LANDIS HESTER

CONTENTS

INTRODUCTION

EVIL FOES LURK IN THE SHADOWS.

Balance is everything. Where there is light, there is darkness. Where there is goodness, evil looms. Over the years, many dangerous foes have tried to take over Ninjago Island, including sneaky snakes, scary skeletons and scurvy pirates. Cruel and cunning as they may be, these fearsome foes are no match for the Ninja's skill, courage, and teamwork.

THE SKELETON ARMY

GET READY TO RATTLE THOSE BONES!

TOUGH BUT DIMWITTED, these boneheaded Skulkins have escaped the Underworld and are ready to destroy Ninjago. Whoever wears the mystical bone helmet that controls these skeletal soldiers has a powerful force at their command. The Skulkins attack with brute force—but not much brainpower.

I'VE GOT A BONE TO PICK WITH YOU

BONEZAI
Bonezai's vehicles and inventions keep the skeletons on the move toward their next target.

FRAKJAW
Like Kai, Frakjaw is strongly linked with the Fire element—but he doesn't have the Ninja's spark of brilliance.

SAMUKAI
This bony bunch is ruled by four-armed Samukai —the ruthless king of the Underworld. Samukai's extra arms and large head make him even spookier-looking than the skeletons he leads— and that's saying something!

CHOPOV
This menacing mechanic uses his simple tools to repair vehicles and slash enemies down to size.

KRUNCHA
Kruncha is one of the more skilled skeletons. He has a knack for driving and a habit for getting into trouble.

WYPLASH
This sneaky skeleton is wiser than most. He also has the creepy ability to turn his head all the way around!

KRAZI
Look out for this battle-crazed Skulkin! From his toes to the tip of his jester's hat, he's focused on one thing: fighting!

NUCKAL
Nuckal is proof that you don't need brilliance to lead: As a general, his main talent is sheer strength.

Catapult arm fires missiles

Scary skull design

Flaming exhaust

SKULL TRUCK
Driven by Nuckal and Kruncha, this rugged vehicle can roll over just about anything. Its huge wheels crunch over tough terrain and its sturdy frame bursts through obstacles—and watch out for bone-crunching ammo being flung from its top arm!

Resilient tires can withstand great speeds

LORD GARMADON

WHO IS LORD GARMADON? He has been many things: An innocent child poisoned by the Great Devourer's bite, a young husband and father, and a power-hungry warlord. Who knows what this complicated character will become next!

BAD BEGINNINGS

As children, Garmadon and Wu trained happily together under the guidance of their father, the First Spinjitzu Master. The brothers became enemies when Garmadon was bitten by a snake and infected with evil.

"MY DARKEST DREAM WILL BECOME REALITY!"
LORD GARMADON

One of four hands for wielding multiple weapons

DATA FILE

* **Known for:**
  Playing dirty
* **Favorite weapon:**
  Garmadon dreams of combining the Golden Weapons into one Megaweapon
* **Likes:**
  Power and glory
* **Dislikes:**
  The Great Devourer

DID YOU KNOW?
Lord Garmadon is a little odd. He eats Condensed Evil (black slime full of maggots) and sunbathes in thunderstorms!

> LEND ME A HAND?

EVIL EVOLUTION

The evil inside Garmadon shows on the outside: venom from the snake that bit him turns his eyes red and gives him terrifying fangs. He once had two arms, but he later grows extra arms as part of his quest to master the four Golden Weapons.

Nin-jo (bamboo stick)

SIBLING RIVALRY

Battles between Sensei Wu and Lord Garmadon are fierce. Blow by blow, spin by spin, these two Spinjitzu masters can match every move the other makes. Who will win in this epic struggle between light and dark, good and evil?

DEVIOUS SCHEMES

Clever Garmadon anticipates the feelings and actions of others—a gift that he uses to trick and sneak his way to power. When he kidnaps Nya, he knows that Kai will come to her rescue, putting the Golden Sword of Fire at risk—exactly what Garmadon wants.

Thunder Bolt weapon

BATTLE AT THE DARK FORTRESS!

A giant skull spider looms over the battle

A BATTLE RAGES for control of four powerful Golden Weapons at Garmadon's Underworld lair. Odds are against the Ninja: Enemy gunners are overhead, giant spiders hang nearby, and Samukai has three of his four hands armed and ready to attack. Can the Ninja and Sensei Wu prevail?

NO ONE MESSES WITH MY SISTER!

GREEDY GARMADON

Garmadon desperately wants to possess the legendary Golden Weapons—but he knows he's not yet strong enough to hold all four at once. Instead, he tricks others into gathering the weapons, fighting off his enemies, and helping him escape the Underworld.

Bones are everywhere in this Underworld fortress

Skull missiles are launched from the tower gunnery

NINJA TO THE RESCUE

The Ninja use their elemental powers to create Spinjitzu tornadoes that flatten their enemies. These swirling forces combine to make an even more powerful weapon: The Tornado of Creation sucks in everything nearby and uses them to create something new.

NYA ESCAPES

Nya was kidnapped to lure the Ninja into this terrible battle—but she's far from helpless. The moment she's free, Nya joins the fight against the Skulkin.

SAMUKAI VS. WU

With two sets of arms, Samukai wields three of the four Golden Weapons— and he's determined to complete the set. Wu must defeat him before he finds the fourth, the Sword of Fire, and masters their power.

THE SERPENTINE

AFTER CENTURIES OF warring amongst themselves, the five Serpentine tribes were entombed underground by the angry residents of Ninjago. Now, a young boy called Lloyd has set them free—and with terrifying powers like these, no one in Ninjago can sleep easily!

> YOU'RE HISSSTORY!

ANACONDRAI

According to legend, this ancient race of snakes is the most powerful and deadly of all. The only surviving member of the species is cunning Pythor. He has the ability to make himself invisible, which he uses to sneak away after convincing others to do his bidding.

> YOU SAY MEAN LIKE IT IS A BAD THING...

VENOMARI

A spray of toxic venom from these green meanies causes weird visions. Victims might think they see a safe path where there isn't one—a dangerous mistake in the deadly toxic bog where the Venomari live.

LOOK INTO MY EYESSS...

HYPNOBRAI

Don't look too closely at these mesmerizing rattlers! One glance into their glowing eyes, and enemies are hypnotized. Then they are forced to do whatever the ssslithering sssnakes sssay. Their general, Skales, is an expert in the snake martial art, Fang-Kwon-Do.

MAYBE WE'VE BITTEN OFF MORE THAN WE CAN CHEW?

SPEAK FOR YOURSELF...

FANGPYRE

A Fangpyre bite gives everything a snakelike appearance—vehicles, Ninja, and even Jay's parents, Ed and Edna! Victims develop an inability to pronounce "s" words without a telltale hiss. The Fangpyre general, Fangtom, even grew an extra head when he bit himself by mistake.

FREE HUGS?

CONSTRICTAI

These powerful snakes torture their foes by wrapping their strong tails around their bodies. They can often be found deep underground, preparing for their next sneak attack, led by their brutish general, Skalidor.

"IT'S ABOUT TIME WE HAD A SERPENTINE BACK IN CHARGE."
SKALIDOR

THE HISTORY OF THE OVERLORD

LONG BEFORE TIME had a name, at the very creation of Ninjago itself, there was good and there was evil—and there is no one more evil than a spirit named the Overlord. Here is his story...

BEGINNINGS

A legendary warrior named the First Spinjitzu Master used the four Golden Weapons to create the land known today as Ninjago.

A PEACEFUL LAND

The First Spinjitzu Master created Ninjago as a peaceful and bountiful land of light. But wherever there is light, there must also be shadow...

DARKNESS LURKS

Out of the shadows, the Overlord was born—shaped by the darkness and born to counterbalance goodness and light.

FIERCE FOES

For many years, the evil, shadowy Overlord menaced the people of Ninjago. The First Spinjitzu Master worked tirelessly to keep the danger at bay, but the Overlord grew stronger—despite his lack of physical form.

MASTER PLAN

Eventually, the Overlord concocted his most terrifying plan yet.
He used his powers to bring to life a number of powerful stone warriors.

THE STONE ARMY RISES

Hungry for power, the Overlord used his Stone Army to challenge the First Spinjitzu Master for control of Ninjago.

A BATTLE RAGES

The First Spinjitzu Master fought bravely against the Overlord and his immense army, but could not destroy his enemy.

A DIFFICULT CHOICE

As the Stone Army overwhelmed him, the First Spinjitzu Master was forced to plunge his sword into the ground and split Ninjago into two.

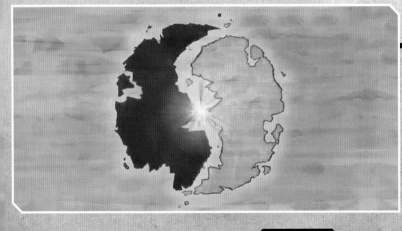

THE LAND DIVIDES

Ninjago was split into two halves: darkness and light. The Overlord was banished to the Dark Island, which sunk beneath the sea, and Ninjago regained its peaceful existence.

THE STONE ARMY

ANCIENT AND INDESTRUCTIBLE, the Stone Army was created by the Overlord for his fight against the First Spinjitzu Master. Luckily for Ninjago, they were then buried deep beneath the earth. Now they have awoken to terrorize the city once more.

> CAN WE PLAY MUSICAL STATUES?

WARRIOR
It is hard to say what is scariest about these stone warriors: their huge helmets or creepy face markings. These fearsome fighters report directly to their general.

SWORDSMAN
The majority of the Stone Army is formed of loyal swordsmen, armed with katanas and conical hats. With endless stamina, these stone figures never stand still for very long.

SCOUT
The scouts make up the lowest rank in the Stone Army. These sneaky characters are expected to be nimble, fast, and remain out of sight when hunting their enemies.

GENERAL KOZU
General Kozu towers over the other stone warriors with his large helmet and extra set of arms. He translates the warrior's ancient language for the Overlord.

LIVING STATUE

Lloyd's mother, Misako, works in Ninjago City's museum, home to a relic of a giant stone warrior. But when venom from the Great Devourer touches the ancient artifact, it comes to life and quickly resumes its task of destruction.

UNBEATABLE STRENGTH

The tough Stone Army are powered by Dark Matter, which make them indestructible so they can withstand fierce attacks. The Ninja will have tough job trying to stop them!

Samurai horns

DID YOU KNOW?

The Stone Army kidnapped an inventor called Dr. Julien and forced him to create weapons and vehicles to use against their enemies.

Sharp side spikes

Single tread at front of vehicle

WARRIOR BIKE

The Stone Army have many weapons and vehicles at their disposal, including this fearsome machine. They use the Warrior Bike to tear around the Dark Island seeking out enemies and attacking intruders.

THE NINDROIDS

INITIATE ATTACK!

THE OVERLORD IS BACK—and he is digital! The Digital Overlord has infected the computer systems that control New Ninjago City and with the help of a robot army, he is planning a technological takeover. His Nindroids are based on Zane's blueprints, but they've been upgraded with increased speed and strength.

GENERAL CRYPTOR

The Nindroid general is heavily armored, with two katanas and advanced programming. In command of the vast Nindroid army and their vehicles and weapons, he enforces the Digital Overlord's orders.

WARRIORS

Nindroid warriors don't need emotions to know where their loyalties lie: They'll follow General Cryptor's orders to their last spark of energy.

DRONES

Drones have very simple programming, so they follow orders without thinking and never lose focus on their mission.

MINDROID

The smallest of the Nindroids, Mindroid is constantly teased by his fellow fighters. This pint-sized fighter has a big point to prove.

CYRUS BORG

Once a force for peace and progress in New Ninjago City, inventor Cyrus Borg has been forced into the service of the Digital Overlord. Borg's own technology was turned against him to modify its kindly creator into a war machine. Borg warned the Ninja about the Overlord before his transformation, but they can't rely on his help now!

DID YOU KNOW?

The Nindroids are based on Zane's blueprints, but they don't contain his unique internal energy source. They rely on external power, so power cuts are bad news for Nindroids!

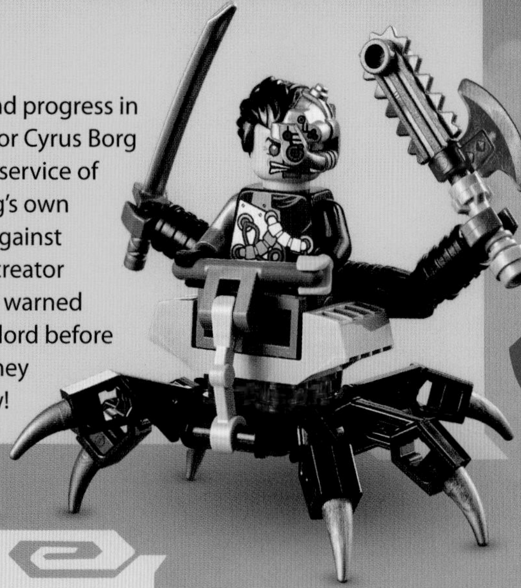

DESTRUCTOID

The name says it all! This Nindroid vehicle is mechanized mayhem. Rolling tracks to go over any terrain, front blasters, an extendable rotating saw, a massive sword and shield—everything about this machine spells trouble.

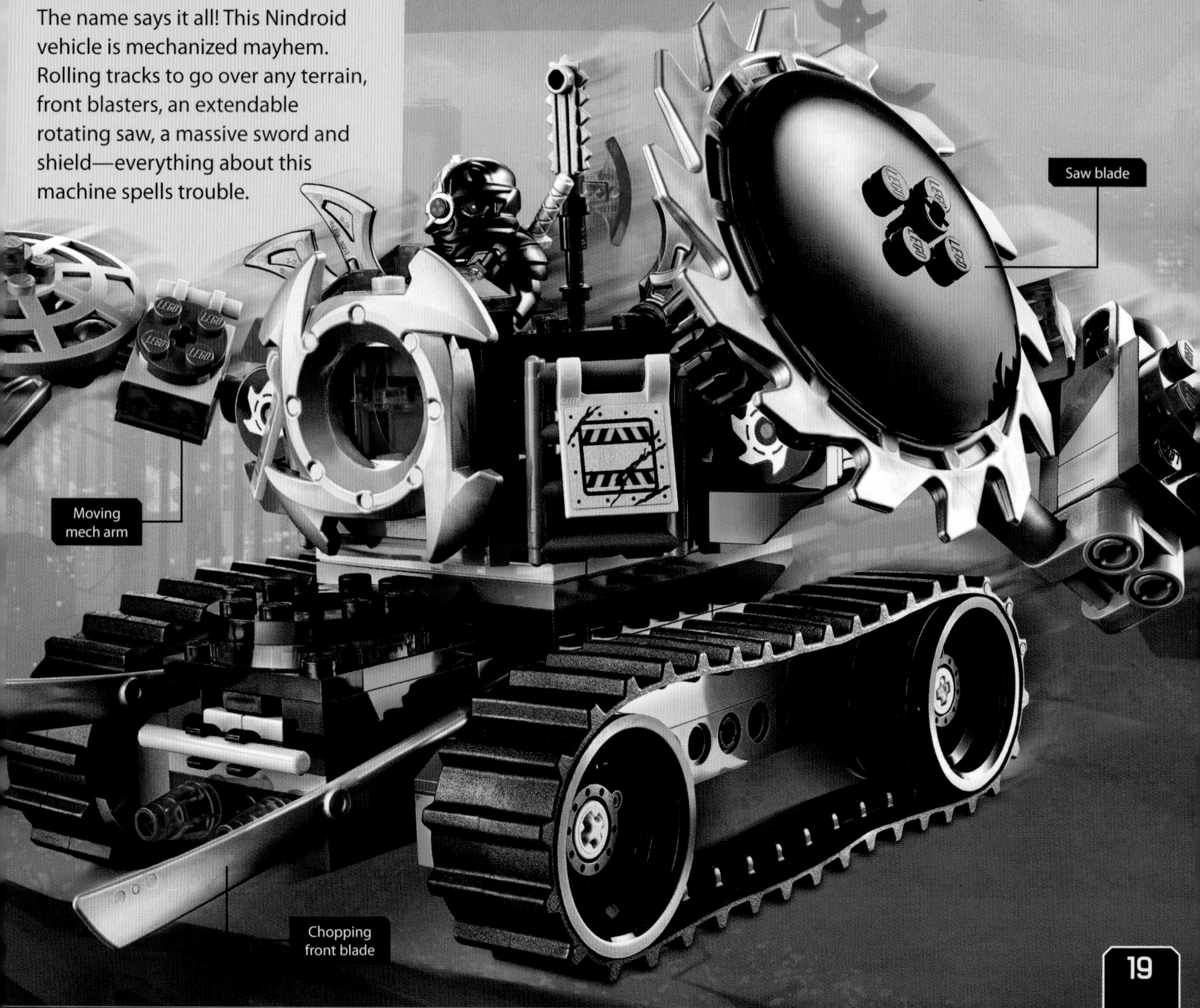

Saw blade
Moving mech arm
Chopping front blade

MASTER CHEN

THE PEOPLE OF NINJAGO know Master Chen as the face of their favorite chain of noodle restaurants. But behind his cheerful front, he's really a scheming master criminal, out to steal the Ninja's powers and unleash chaos on Ninjago.

NOODLE HOUSE

What could be more innocent than a delicious dinner? Master Chen's restaurants are known for tasty bowls of noodles and the giant winking Chen sign above the door. His customers don't know about Chen's devious plans to take over Ninjago.

> FORGET NOODLES, I WANT POWER

DATA FILE

- **Known for:** His chain of Noodle House restaurants
- **Favorite weapon:** The Staff of Elements
- **Likes:** Power and deceit
- **Dislikes:** Anyone who wants to stand in his way

"I HOLD ALL THE CARDS!"
MASTER CHEN

> I'LL KEEP AN EYE OUT.

DADDY'S GIRL?

Chen's daughter, Skylor, is used to her father's trickery and schemes, so it is no surprise when he orders her to spy on the Ninja. But there's more to Skylor than following orders: She has the ability to absorb the powers of others—and maybe even to make some powerful choices of her own.

STAFF OF ELEMENTS

Master Chen's staff was made from crystals from the caves of his secret island. Each time a contestant in his tournament is defeated, the staff can collect the fighter's powers, making it even more powerful—and dangerous—with every battle.

Bulky build isn't sleek, but it is strong

ANACONDRAI COPTER

Chen has spent years building his army, including some Anacondrai equipment sure to have enemies on the run: This Serpentine flyer packs some frightening firepower, and lets Chen enjoy all the mayhem from high in the air.

DID YOU KNOW?
The noodles in Chen's restaurants are made by imprisoned workers on his secret island.

THE ANACONDRAI

MASTER CHEN

Master Chen has one dream: to become one with the Anacondrai and begin a new reign of terror in Ninjago! Each of his followers has a purple snake tattoo to show their loyalty to Chen and his cause.

OF ALL THE slithery snakes in Ninjago, one tribe is the most dangerous. Known as the fiercest fighters in Serpentine history, the Anacondrai were banished to the Underworld long ago—but if Master Chen has his way, they'll soon be back!

> I'VE GOT A FANGTASTIC PLAN

CLOUSE

Chen's second in command, Clouse, used to be Garmadon's training partner—but only Garmadon achieved the title of Lord. Now Clouse wants to get revenge on Garmadon for outshining him all those years ago.

ZUGU

Zugu is the perfect guard for Master Chen's underground noodle factory: He's tough, willing to follow orders without question, and will do anything for food!

EYEZOR

He has just one working eye—but Eyezor can spot ways to create mayhem wherever he looks. Mean, mohawked, and dead-set on making his enemies suffer, Eyezor is the perfect sidekick for Chen's destructive plans.

CHOPE-CHOPE

Chope-Chope invented his own name to seem menacing—although some would say his scary grimace and ruthless fighting style are quite enough for that!

SLEVEN

Sleven is more than willing to go along with Chen's plans to take on Anacondrai powers. This slithery guy already acts like a snake, he just needs a tail to complete his image!

KAPAU

Like Chope-Chope, Kapau renamed himself to sound tough and scary. Their plan worked—both friends are rising in the ranks of Chen's army, whether or not their skills deserve it.

KRAIT

As a loyal footsoldier in Chen's Army, Krait is dedicated to squashing Chen's enemies, helping steal the Elemental Masters' powers, and completing the army's Anacondrai transformation—no questions asked.

PYTHOR

Pythor is a true Anacondrai—vital to Chen's plan of transforming his army into snake-like warriors. His misadventures have left him bleached white, but his devious mind is still full of colorful plans.

Anacondrai warrior sword

ANACONDRAI CRUSHER

This Anacondrai Crusher has massive jaws—making it a frightening sight to anyone who crosses its path. It has spinning blades, a slashing tail, striking speed, and its bite is just as deadly as it looks.

Spinning blade rotors

Tribal printing on wheels

TO RAISE AN
ANACONDRAI ARMY YOU MUST:

PLAN AN EXCITING TOURNAMENT AS A DIVERSION

ATTRACT ELEMENTAL MASTERS TO A REMOTE LOCATION

STEAL POWERS FROM THE MASTERS TO COMPLETE AN ANCIENT SPELL

WATCH YOUR ARMY TRANSFORM INTO MENACING SERPENTS!

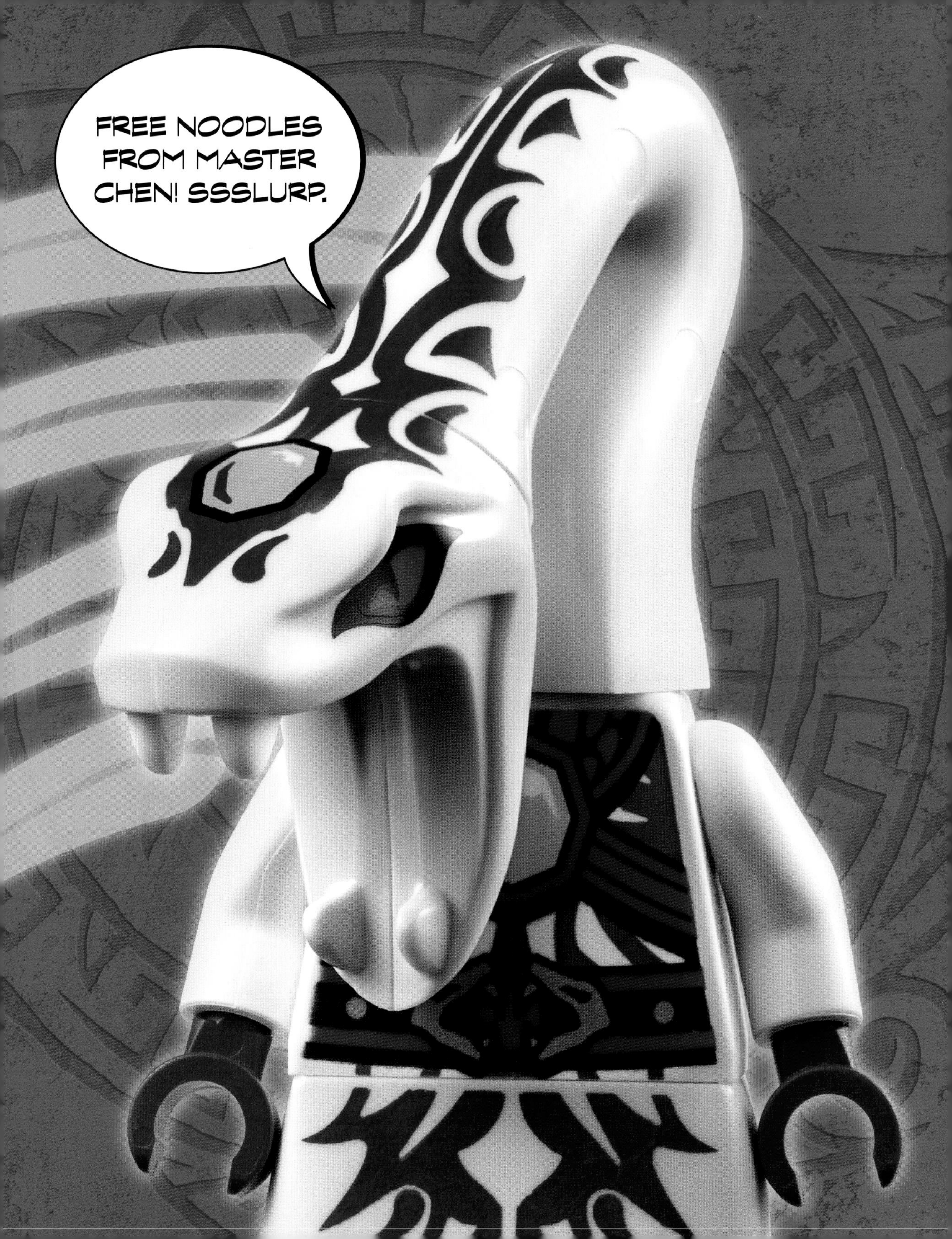
FREE NOODLES FROM MASTER CHEN! SSSLURP.

THREATS TO NINJAGO

THE NINJA HAVE battled so many enemies, sometimes it's tough to keep track of them all—especially when they keep switching sides! It's a good job the Ninja keep files on some of Ninjago's biggest villains.

SKELETONS
Alias: Skulkins
Wanted for: Attempted theft (Golden Weapons), general mayhem
Status: Unknown

LLOYD GARMADON
Alias: The Green Ninja, The Golden Ninja
Wanted for: Theft (candy), truancy, trying to resurrect a snake army
Status: Reformed

PYTHOR
Alias: Pythor P. Chumsworth
Wanted for: Theft (sealife), kidnapping, endangering the public, breaking and entering
Status: Active

NINDROID

Alias: Mini-Nindroid
Wanted for: Aiding and abetting the Overlord, underage possession of weapons
Status: Powered down

LORD GARMADON

Alias: Sensei Garmadon
Wanted for: Endangering the public, theft, driving an unlicensed vehicle
Status: Reformed

SKYLOR

Alias: Miss Chen
Wanted for: Espionage, theft (elemental powers)
Status: At large, possibly reformed

MORRO

Alias: Unknown
Wanted for: Suspected evil activity, plans unknown
Status: Serious risk to Ninjago

Penguin
Random
House

EDITORS Pamela Afram, Matt Jones,
Clare Millar, Rosie Peet
SENIOR DESIGNERS Jo Connor, David McDonald
SENIOR SLIPCASE DESIGNER Mark Penfound
EDITORIAL ASSISTANT Beth Davies
DESIGNED BY Dynamo
COVER DESIGNER Stefan Georgiou
PRE-PRODUCTION PRODUCER Kavita Varma
SENIOR PRODUCER Lloyd Robertson
MANAGING EDITOR Paula Regan
DESIGN MANAGERS Guy Harvey, Jo Connor
CREATIVE MANAGER Sarah Harland
PUBLISHER Julie Ferris
ART DIRECTOR Lisa Lanzarini
PUBLISHING DIRECTOR Simon Beecroft

Additional photography by Gary Ombler

Dorling Kindersley would like to thank:
Heike Bornhausen, Randi Sørensen,
Martin Leighton and Paul Hansford
at the LEGO Group; Radhika Banerjee, Jon Hall,
and Pamela Shiels at DK for design assistance.

This edition published in 2017
First American Edition, 2016
Published in the United States by DK Publishing
345 Hudson Street, New York, New York 10014

www.LEGO.com/ninjago
www.dk.com

DK, a Division of Penguin Random House LLC

Contains content previously published in LEGO®
NINJAGO® *Secret World of the Ninja* (2015)

003-298874-Jul/2017

Page design copyright © 2017 Dorling Kindersley Limited

A catalog record for this book is available from
the Library of Congress.

ISBN: 978-5-0010-1404-1

Printed in Heshan, China

A WORLD OF IDEAS:
SEE ALL THERE IS TO KNOW